benjamin britten

Six Metamorphoses after Ovid, Op. 49

oboe solo

BOOSEY & HAWKES

Boosey & Hawkes Music Publishers Limited

for Joy Boughton

Six Metamorphoses after Ovid

for Oboe Solo

I. PAN who played upon the reed pipe which was Syrinx, his beloved.

BENJAMIN BRITTEN, Op. 49

© Copyright 1952 by Hawkes & Son (London) Ltd.

Printed in England

B. & H. **17985**

II. PHAETON who rode upon the chariot of the sun for one day and was hurled into the river Padus by a thunderbolt.

B. & H. 17985

III. NIOBE who, lamenting the death of her fourteen children, was turned into a mountain.

Andante ♩ = 60

mf piangendo

B. & H. 17985

IV. BACCHUS

at whose feasts is heard the noise of gaggling women's
tattling tongues and shouting out of boys.

V. NARCISSUS who fell in love with his own image and became a flower.

*From this point the notes with upward stems represent the reflected image of Narcissus, and those with downward stems Narcissus himself.

B. & H. 17985

VI. ARETHUSA who, flying from the love of Alpheus the river god, was turned into a fountain.

B. & H. 17985

Printed by Halstan:
Halstan UK, 2-10 Plantation Road, Amersham, Bucks, HP6 6HJ. United Kingdom
Halstan DE, Weißliliengasse 4, 55116 Mainz. Germany

MUSIC FOR WOODWIND ENSEMBLE

SIX SONATAS CPE Bach *(cl., bsn., hpchd.)*
Six elegant sonatas with optional parts for violin and cello.

ESPRIT RUDE/ESPRIT DOUX Elliott Carter *(fl., cl.)*
Written for Pierre Boulez's 60th birthday in 1985. Inspired by classical Greek words represented motivically in the work.

17th CENTURY HUNGARIAN DANCES Ferenc Farkas
(fl., ob., cl., hn., bsn.)
Five characterful dances in a variety of moods.

WALTZ AND INTERLUDE Clare Grundman *(fl., cl., pf.)*
An entertaining trio by one of America's best-known composers for band.

SONATINE André Jolivet *(fl., cl.)*
SONATINE André Jolivet *(ob., bsn.)*
Challenging works, in two unusual duet combinations.

DUET-CONCERTINO Richard Strauss *(cl., bsn., pf.)*
A substantial work, written in 1947. This edition contains a piano reduction of the original string orchestra and harp accompaniment.

FOUR WALTZES Dmitri Shostakovich *(fl./picc., cl., pf.)*
Pieces in Shostakovich's lighter style, depicting Spring, a joke and a barrel organ.

SIX SONATES CPE Bach *(clarinette, basson, clavecin)*
Six sonates pleines d'élégance avec parties facultatives de violon et de violoncelle.

ESPRIT RUDE/ESPRIT DOUX Elliott Carter *(flûte, clarinette)*
Ecrit pour le 60ème anniversaire de Pierre Boulez en 1985. Inspiré par les termes classiques grecs qui sont représentés dans les motifs dont se compose l'œuvre.

DANSES HONGROISES DU 17ÈME SIÈCLE Ferenc Farkas
(flûte, hautbois, clarinette, cor, basson)
Cinq danses pleines d'esprit, dans des caractères très différents.

VALSE ET INTERLUDE Clare Grundman
(flûte, clarinette, piano)
Un trio divertissant par l'un des compositeurs américains les plus célèbres pour ensembles d'instruments à vent.

SONATINE André Jolivet *(flûte, clarinette)*
SONATINE André Jolivet *(hautbois, basson)*
Des œuvres qui offrent un véritable défi pour deux duos inhabituels.

DUO CONCERTANT Richard Strauss
(clarinette, basson, piano)
Une œuvre importante écrite en 1947. Cette édition contient un accompagnement pour piano arrangé à partir de l'original pour orchestre à cordes et harpe.

QUATRE VALSES Dimitri Chostakovitch
(flûte/piccolo, clarinette, piano)
Des morceaux dans le style léger de Chostakovitch qui décrivent le Printemps, une plaisanterie et un orgue de barbarie.

SECHS SONATEN CPE Bach *(Klar., Fg., Cemb.)*
Sechs elegante Sonaten, wahlweise mit Parts für Violine und Cello.

ESPRIT RUDE/ESPRIT DOUX Elliott Carter *(Fl., Klar.)*
Zum sechzigsten Geburtstag von Pierre Boulez 1985 geschrieben. Inspiriert von einem Text aus der griechischen Antike, der in dem Werk motivisch umgesetzt wird.

UNGARISCHE TÄNZE DES 17. JAHRHUNDERTS
Ferenc Farkas *(Fl., Ob., Klar., Hr., Fg.)*
Fünf stilvolle Tänze mit verschiedenartiger Atmosphäre.

WALZER UND ZWISCHENSPIEL Clare Grundman
(Fl., Klar., Kl.)
Ein unterhaltsames Trio von einem den bekanntesten amerikanischen Komponisten für Blaskapelle.

SONATINE André Jolivet *(Fl., Klar.)*
SONATINE André Jolivet *(Ob., Fg.)*
Anspruchsvolle Werke in zwei ungewöhnlichen Duettkombinationen.

DUETT-CONCERTINO Richard Strauss *(Klar., Fg., Kl.)*
Ein gewichtiges Werk, entstanden 1947. Die vorliegende Ausgabe umfaßt einen Klavierauszug der Originalbegleitung für Streichorchester und Harfe.

VIER WALZER Dmitri Schostakowitsch
(Fl./Pikkolo, Klar., Kl.)
Stücke in Schostakowitschs leichterem Stil, in denen der Frühling, ein Scherz und eine Drehorgel dargestellt werden.

BOOSEY & HAWKES

Boosey & Hawkes Music Publishers Limited

www.boosey.com

Ad. 290

Selected Works for

Oboe

and Cor Anglais

Ad 465